POKÉMON DETECTIVE PIKACHU

MOVIE JOURNAL

CONTENTS

DETECTIVE
PIKACHU

WELCOME TO RYME CITY!

On the neon streets of Ryme City, people live in harmony alongside Pokémon. This thriving metropolis is buzzing with activity. But strange things are simmering under the surface... What could be going on in the shadows?

THE BIG CITY!

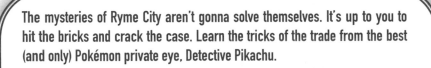

The mysteries of Ryme City aren't gonna solve themselves. It's up to you to hit the bricks and crack the case. Learn the tricks of the trade from the best (and only) Pokémon private eye, Detective Pikachu.

With you analyzing evidence and Detective Pikachu getting the word on the street from other Pokémon, you can get to the bottom of everything going on in the big city. Discover the clues, hear from all the witnesses and solve cases!

SERVING UP SMILES

The Hi-Hat Cafe serves up the best coffee in town. Draw a picture of your favourite place to recharge after a long day collecting clues.

Detective Pikachu loves a hot cup o' joe! What are your favourite foods and drinks?

HI-HAT
CAFE

IN THE SHADOWS

It's a dark night in Ryme City and these Pokémon are skulking in the shadows.
Can you identify each Pokémon?

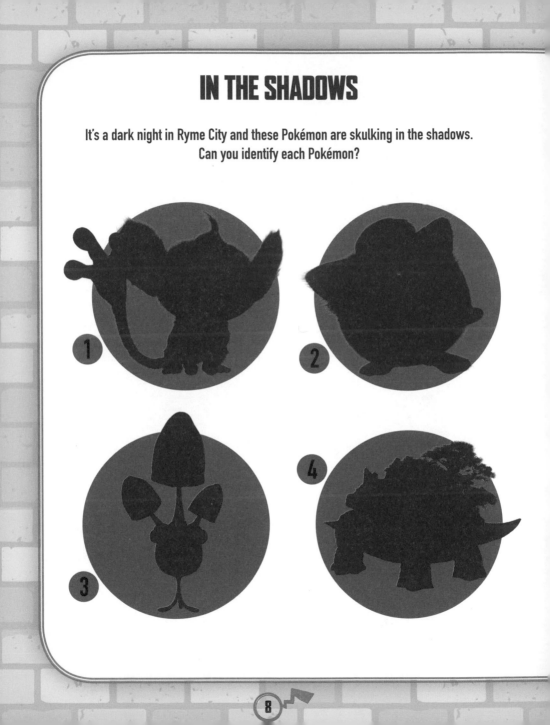

SUPER SIGNS

There are lots of bright lights in the big city. Design your own colourful sign to light up the neon streets.

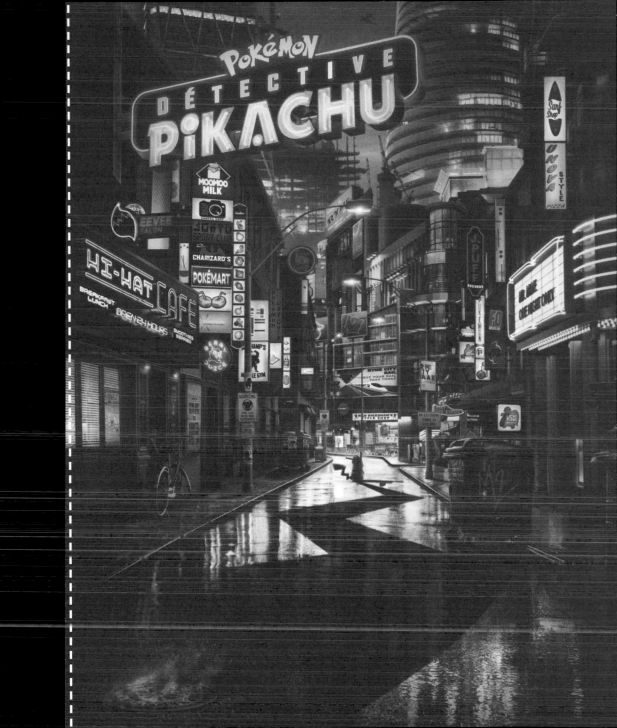

MEET THE
POKÉMON!

Pokémon come in all shapes and sizes — they're unique, just like you!
Each individual Pokémon has its own personality — there are a lot of
Pikachu, but there's only one great Detective Pikachu!

POKÉMON PARADISE

Discover more about the Pokémon who roam the neon streets of Ryme City.
From the snuggleable Snubbull to the lively Ludicolo, the city's scene is electric!

My favourite Pokémon is:

_____

I like this Pokémon because:

_____

Draw a picture of your favourite Pokémon.

DETECTIVE PIKACHU

Watching over the weird and wonderful goings-on in Ryme City is a Pokémon like no other: Detective Pikachu, an adorable super-sleuth who is a mystery even to himself.

Name: **Pikachu**
Type: **Electric**
Category: **Mouse Pokémon**
Height: **1'04" (0.4 m)**
Weight: **13.2 lbs (6.0 kg)**

A LITTLE CUTENESS IN A BIG CITY!

Draw and colour Detective Pikachu in the grid below. Try copying the picture section by section.

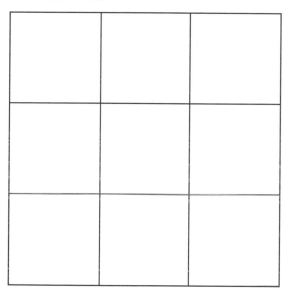

PSYDUCK

Psyduck is often terribly confused, so it's no surprise that Ryme City's mysteries are giving it an even worse headache than normal.

Name: **Psyduck**
Type: **Water**
Category: **Duck Pokémon**
Height: **2'07" (0.8 m)**
Weight: **43.2 lbs (19.6 kg)**

What is a mystery in your life? Are you ready to solve it? Write about it here.

LOUDRED

Get ready to cover your ears! When Loudred wants to be heard,
its ears really amplify the message.

Name: **Loudred**
Type: **Normal**
Category: **Big Voice Pokémon**
Height: **3'03" (1.0 m)**
Weight: **89.3 lbs (40.5 kg)**

Write down three things that you would like to shout about —
it could be a pet peeve or something you're really excited about.

1. _____

_____

_____

2. _____

_____

_____

3. _____

_____

_____

SNUBBULL

Fearsome or friendly, the trouble with Snubbull is that it might look scary, but this Pokémon is a big softie at heart. A little shy at first, Snubbull can be a fierce friend.

Name: **Snubbull**
Type: **Fairy**
Category: **Fairy Pokémon**
Height: **2'00" (0.6 m)**
Weight: **17.2 lbs (7.8 kg)**

Every good detective knows that looks can be deceiving.
Don't let Snubbull's fangs frighten you away.

Draw your very own cute companion – super snuggleable!

MR. MIME

This mysterious Pokémon is a skilled performer. You won't believe your eyes, until you walk into one of his walls. If you're not impressed with his show, you'll get hit with a double slap!

Name: **Mr. Mime**
Type: **Psychic-Fairy**
Category: **Barrier Pokémon**
Height: **4'03" (1.3 m)**
Weight: **120.1 lbs (54.5 kg)**

Mr. Mime communicates through pantomime. What do you have to say?
Stick a photo of you holding your best pantomime pose here,
and then write down what it means.

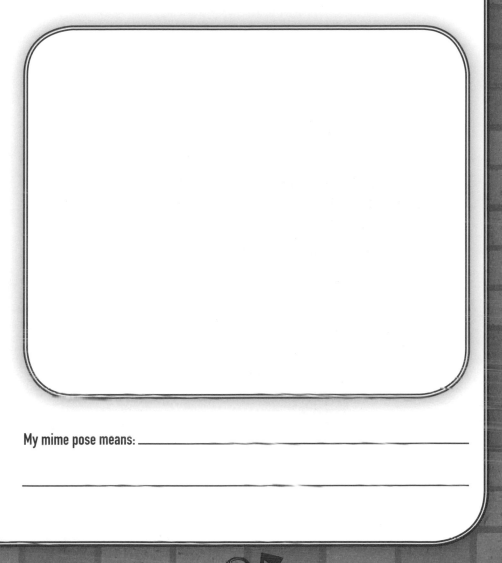

My mime pose means: _____

_____

LUDICOLO

Ludicolo feel compelled to move to the rhythm when they hear festive music. You can find this Pokémon dancing behind the counter and serving up smiles at the Hi-Hat Cafe.

Name: **Ludicolo**
Type: **Water-Grass**
Category: **Carefree Pokémon**
Height: **4'11" (1.5 m)**
Weight: **121.3 lbs (55.0 kg)**

Using the words around the page to inspire you, write a song or rap
about one of your great adventures or exciting mysteries.

FRIENDS

ADVENTURE

DANCE

PARTY

NEON

CITY

MORELULL

This Pokémon can illuminate any situation, but get your answers quickly before it sends you off to dreamland.

> Keep this book by your bed, so you can scribble down your dreams as soon as you wake up.

Name: **Morelull**
Type: **Grass-Fairy**
Category: **Illuminating Pokémon**
Height: **0'08" (0.2 m)**
Weight: **3.3 lbs (1.5 kg)**

DREAM BIG

The dreams you have when you're asleep can have surprising and powerful meanings.
You might even crack a case whilst you're drifting off!

Record a whole week of your dreams here.

Monday

Tuesday

Wednesday

Thursday

Friday

Saturday

Sunday

Draw a picture or write about the best dream you've ever had:

BULBASAUR

These little Pokémon can be found soaking up the sun in the great outdoors. Don't be fooled by their cute appearance, though — Bulbasaur are more than capable of defending themselves!

Name: **Bulbasaur**
Type: **Grass-Poison**
Category: **Seed Pokémon**
Height: **2'04"(0.7 m)**
Weight: **15.2 lbs (6.9 kg)**

Each time you have a creative thought write or draw it here.
Use this page to plant the seed and watch your ideas grow.

ARCANINE

Beautiful and majestic, Arcanine uses the flame that burns within it as fuel to run amazing distances. Arcanine is one of the fastest Pokémon there is — are you ready to turn up the heat with Arcanine before it makes a quick getaway?

Name: Arcanine
Type: Fire
Category: Legendary Pokémon
Height: 6'03" (1.9 m)
Weight: 341.7 lbs (155.0 kg)

As a top detective, it is important to keep your mind sharp.

Name three tools that a detective needs for an investigation:

1. _____

2. _____

3. _____

Write down three questions to ask your witness:

1. _____

2. _____

3. _____

Now some food for thought! Can you solve this puzzling Pokémon riddle?

When things aren't going right, this happy little Pokémon is cheery and bright.
On the neon streets, it's dark at night, but this super-sleuth is a shining light.

_____

ANSWER: Detective Pikachu.

MACHAMP

Machamp's four arms make it an incredibly powerful fighter and handy to have around when there's trouble brewing.

Name: **Machamp**
Type: **Fighting**
Category: **Superpower Pokémon**
Height: **5'03" (1.6 m)**
Weight: **286.6 lbs (130.0 kg)**

Machamp is known for being strong and liking a challenge.
What are five challenges you hope to master? Write them down here.

1

2

3

4

5

TORTERRA

Torterra is a big Pokémon in a big city! Smaller Pokémon have been known to build their nests upon its large shell.

Name: **Torterra**
Type: **Grass-Ground**
Category: **Continent Pokémon**
Height: **7'03" (2.2 m)**
Weight: **683.4 lbs (310.0 kg)**

Just as smaller Pokémon might build a home on Torterra's shell, all good detectives build a hideout for themselves. What's your hideout like? Draw it below!

JIGGLYPUFF

Be careful when looking into its cute, round eyes, this adorable Pokémon can lull people to sleep with its mysterious melody.

Name: **Jigglypuff**
Type: **Normal-Fairy**
Category: **Balloon Pokémon**
Height: **1'08" (0.5 m)**
Weight: **12.1 lbs (5.5 kg)**

Jigglypuff isn't the only Pokémon to hold a tune!

What's your favourite kind of music? Write down three of your favourite songs.

1. _____

2. _____

3. _____

If you were in a band, what would it be called?

_____

Now design an amazing cover
for your very own album.

AIPOM

This playful Pokémon is always monkeying around! Aipom uses its strong tail to swing through the streets of Ryme City.

Name: **Aipom**
Type: **Normal**
Category: **Long Tail Pokémon**
Height: **2'07" (0.8 m)**
Weight: **25.4 lbs (11.5 kg)**

Aipom often has a cheeky smile on its face. Draw a picture or stick photos of you on your own detective adventure.

CHARIZARD

Charizard is a winged wonder and can breathe fire. But watch out for its flames — the superhot temperature can melt almost anything!

Name: **Charizard**
Type: **Fire-Flying**
Category: **Flame Pokémon**
Height: **5'07" (1.7 m)**
Weight: **199.5 lbs (90.5 kg)**

Ryme City is a place where people and Pokémon live together in harmony, but there have been reports of rampaging Pokémon in Ryme City. One way to stay calm is to think happy thoughts!

Write down your three favourite memories.

1. _____

2. _____

3. _____

Now put your detective hat on and see if you can work out why they're your favourite memories — maybe they have something in common.

1. _____

2. _____

3. _____

SNORLAX

Naptime is any time for this Pokémon! Snorlax's loud snores can be heard over the hustle and bustle of Ryme City's busy streets.

Name: **Snorlax**
Type: **Normal**
Category: **Sleeping Pokémon**
Height: **6'11" (2.1 m)**
Weight: **1014.1 lbs (460.0 kg)**

Even the noise of Ryme City can't keep this Pokémon awake for long. When it's not busy eating, Snorlax is busy sleeping.

Write down three of your favourite things to do in your spare time.

1. _____

2. _____

3. _____

When you're not busy collecting clues and tailing suspects, how do you like to relax? Draw a picture or stick a photo of you and your friends hanging out.

MEWTWO

The mysterious and elusive Mewtwo is a new face to Ryme City's people and Pokémon...
Where did it come from? What does it want? Can it really be as powerful as it seems?

Name: **Mewtwo**
Type: **Psychic**
Category: **Genetic Pokémon**
Height: **6'07" (2.0 m)**
Weight: **269.0 lbs (122.0 kg)**

Mewtwo is a mighty Pokémon with amazing powers. There are so many special things about you, too. Write about them here.

People always go to you for help with:

_____

You give really great advice about:

_____

A time when you were proud of yourself:

_____

People often compliment you on:

_____

Do you have a hidden talent?

_____

With so many Pokémon that may be involved in Detective Pikachu's investigation, it's important for you to know more about the residents of Ryme City. Write down a fun fact you've discovered about each Pokémon.

PSYDUCK

_____

_____

LOUDRED

_____

_____

SNUBBULL

_____

_____

MR. MIME

_____

_____

LUDICOLO

_____

_____

MORELULL

_____

_____

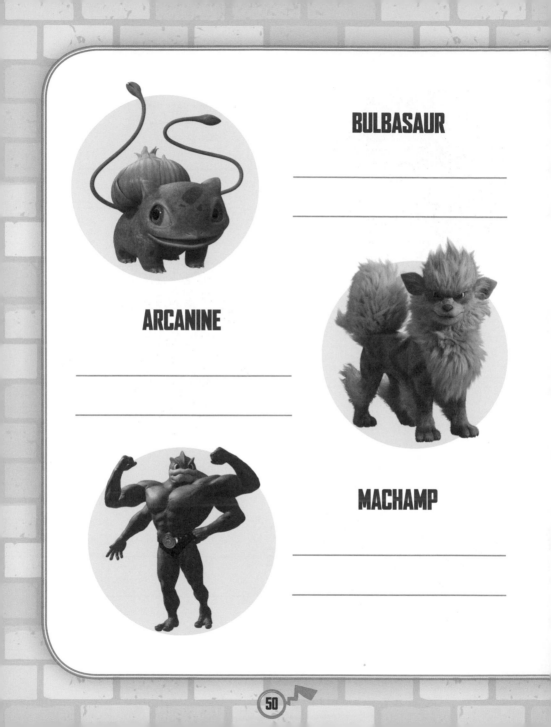

BULBASAUR

ARCANINE

MACHAMP

TORTERRA

_____

_____

JIGGLYPUFF

_____

_____

AIPOM

_____

_____

BECOME A
DETECTIVE!

There are hundreds of Pokémon living in Ryme City with amazing talents and skills. There are so many special things about you that make you awesome, too. It's time to discover more about your detective abilities and set up your own detective agency.

YOUR CASE FILE

Before you start collecting clues and solving mysteries, it's time to discover more about you.
This is your journal, so use the space below to fill in all about you and your life.

NAME: _____

NICKNAME: _____

AGE: _____

DATE OF BIRTH: _____

LIST THREE OF YOUR BEST SKILLS:

1. _____

2. _____

3. _____

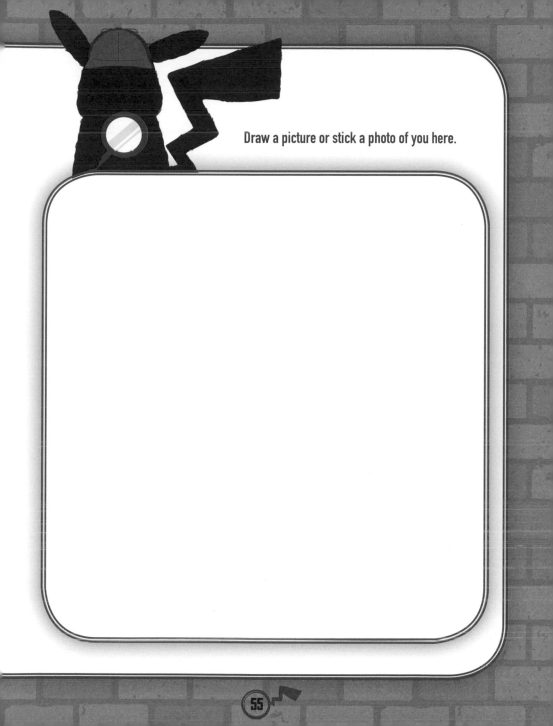

Draw a picture or stick a photo of you here.

SHOCKING DISCOVERIES

Detective Pikachu isn't just a lightning-tailed crime-solving detective,
he's lightning fast, too! How about you?

Write down all your answers about your favourite things as quickly as
you can below. The quicker you do it, the more likely your answers are going
to be honest and accurate. You may be shocked by what you discover.

My Favourite...

Book:

_____

Treat:

_____

Sport:

_____

Pokémon:

_____

Film:

_____

Place:

_____

Outfit:

_____

Game:

_____

Colour:

_____

Shop:

_____

Song:

_____

Day:

_____

Weather:

_____

Now you can practise your interview technique by asking your friends and family the same questions.

PERSONAL PUZZLES

You've learned about some of the amazing Pokémon who live in Ryme City,
now it's time to discover more about yourself!

What would you like to be when you grow up?

I would like to be: _____

_____

_____

_____

Because: _____

_____

_____

_____

_____

Where would you choose to go on your next adventure?

I would like to go to: _____

_____

_____

Because: _____

_____

Unfortunately, you can't become all the Pokémon, unless you're a shape-shifting Ditto! Which Pokémon would you like to be?

I would like to be: _____

_____

_____

Because: _____

_____

PARTNER UP

Which Pokémon is your partner in Ryme? Draw it below.

Name: _____

Type is the key to unlocking a Pokémon's power. A Pokémon's type can tell you a lot about it — from where to find it in the wild to the moves it'll be able to use in a tight spot.

Type: _____

Knowledge is power! Write down everything you need to know about your Pokémon here.

Description: _____

_____

_____

_____

What amazing skills does your Pokémon have?

Moves: _____

_____

_____

_____

_____

ROLE MODEL

A role model is someone who sets a good example for you to follow. A crime-solving detective can be a great role model to have... but maybe you have someone else in mind! Write about a special person you admire and respect.

The name of my role model is: _____

I admire them because: _____

_____

_____

_____

Three strengths they have that I admire are:

1. _____

2. _____

3. _____

Draw or stick a picture of your role model here.

Your role model can be real or from a story, a family member, celebrity
or even your favourite Pokémon, like Detective Pikachu!

DARING DETECTIVE

Be inspired by the lightning-tailed crime solver, Detective Pikachu, and master your own mysteries. Get ready to shock your friends with your super sleuthing skills!

To help you on your way to becoming a master detective, you'll need two things:

1. A location to use as your base

All good detectives need an office where they can plan their investigations. When choosing your hideaway, remember it should be away from prying eyes and have enough space for you to work on your cases. It's also a good idea to have somewhere to store evidence.

Where my detective office will be:

_____

Now draw a picture!

2. A detective club

It's a lot more fun to set up your detective agency, plan investigations and learn sleuthing skills with a group of friends. When recruiting fellow detectives, remember to choose people you can trust.

Who will be in my detective club:

CONFIDENTIAL

CALLING CARD

When there's a spark of trouble and mysteries need to be solved, people need to know that you'll be there to help. Create a calling card for your own detective agency so people know how to find you.

Name of your detective agency: _____

Design a logo for your own detective agency.

Now add your logo to your detective card and fill in your details.

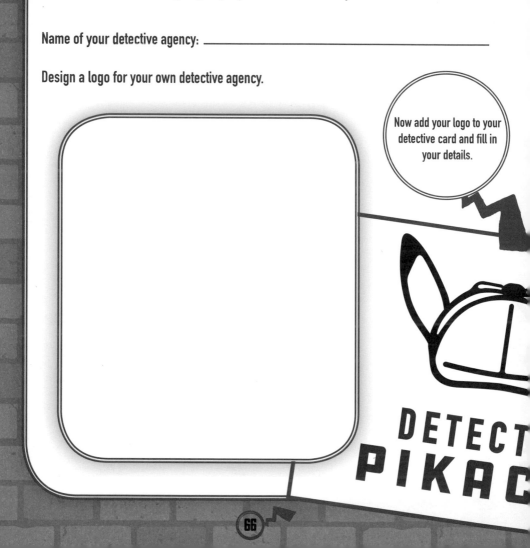

DETECT
PIKAC

ON THE CASE

When you're busy following the clues, it's easy to get caught up in the whirlwind of the big city. A good detective is always aware of their environment and what's going on around them.

You'll need to know your way around to help you get to the bottom of your investigation. Practise your observation skills by describing an important location.

Location:

_____

Name three key features:

_____

What has changed since you were last here?

_____

_____

_____

_____

Draw a map of your town or city. Try including some of the big landmarks to help you along the way.

PARTNERS IN RYME

Every investigator needs a trusted buddy by their side. Detective Pikachu found his perfect partner, Tim Goodman. Together, they hit the bricks and follow the clues to crack the case. Who would you choose to help you solve mysteries and crack cases?

Name:

How did you meet your partner in Ryme?

List three of their best skills:

1.

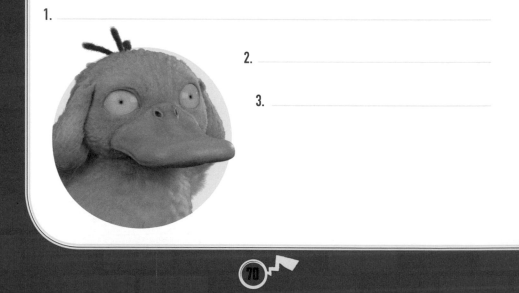

2.

3.

Draw a picture or stick a photo of your sidekick.

MASTER DETECTIVE

When Pikachu talks most people just hear 'Pika, Pika', but this cunning creature has a real way with words. Write down your own amazing catchphrase to say when you crack a case.

My catchphrase is: _____

_____

_____

_____

My catchphrase means: _____

_____

_____

_____

_____

Detective Pikachu always looks the part with his detective hat.
Draw a picture or stick a photo of you in your own detective outfit.

COLLECTING CLUES

Detective Pikachu is searching for clues all over Ryme City. What do you think
he might uncover about you?

Something you're scared of:

_____

Something only your best friend knows:

_____

Something good you've done that no one knows about:

_____

Something you've never told anyone:

_____

Something uncool that you secretly like:

_____

DETECTIVE
PIKACHU

SOLVE A
MYSTERY!

Get ready to put your detective knowledge to the test with your favourite Pokémon private eye. Use your super sleuthing skills to collect the clues and become a master detective. It's time to hit the streets of Ryme City and crack the case!

MYSTERY MISSION

It seems like everyone Detective Pikachu crosses paths with in Ryme City has a story to tell. Use your imagination and write your own mystery story. Has your Pokémon gone missing, or maybe your best friend?

Title of your story:

_____

Write it here:

_____

_____

_____

_____

_____

If you run out of space, finish your story on some lined paper.

TOP TEAM

The streets of Ryme City can be a dangerous place — people and Pokémon disappear without a trace! If you were putting a mystery-solving team together, which Pokémon would you want to join you and why?

Name: _____

I would choose this Pokémon because:

_____

_____

Draw a picture of your Pokémon partner here.

Name: _____

I would choose this Pokémon because:

_____

_____

_____

_____

_____

Draw a picture of your Pokémon partner here.

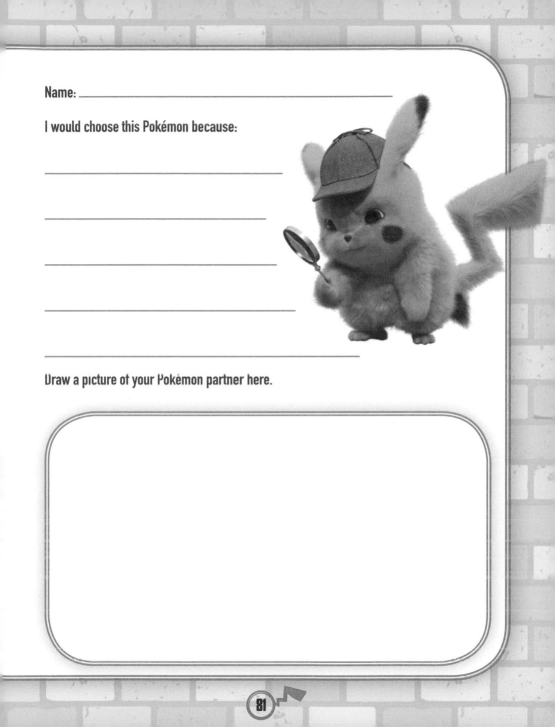

LIGHTNING QUIZ

How much do you know about the lightning-tailed crime solver? Don't worry if you don't know the answers — you can find out everything you need to know in this book.

1. Fill in the blanks. Detective Pikachu has a _____ shaped tail.

a) Thunder
b) Circle
c) Triangle
d) Lightning

2. Where does Detective Pikachu live?

a) Celestic Town
b) Ryme City
c) Twinleaf Town
d) Pastoria City

3. Fill in the blanks. Detective Pikachu is a _____ Pokémon.

a) Electric type
b) Mouse type
c) Thunder type
d) Pikachu type

4. Who is Detective Pikachu's partner in Ryme?

a) Rich Wakehall
b) Tim Goodman
c) Tom Goodword
d) Alex Wrightman

5. Where does Detective Pikachu store his electric energy?

a) In his tail
b) Under his hat
c) In his cheeks
d) In his nose

6. What is Detective Pikachu's favourite drink?

a) Tea
b) Coffee
c) Water
d) Fruit juice

Use a pencil to fill in your answers, and then you can do the quiz again or test a friend!

ANSWERS: 1-d, 2-b, 3-a, 4-b, 5- c, 6-b.

SHOCKINGLY ADORABLE

Detective Pikachu is a spark in the shadows of Ryme City.
Write down three things you love about this super-sleuth.

1. _____

2. _____

3. _____

Stay positive! Now write down three things that you like about yourself.

1. _____

2. _____

3. _____

BRIGHT IDEAS

Use this space to write down any notes or top-secret observations
from your investigations.

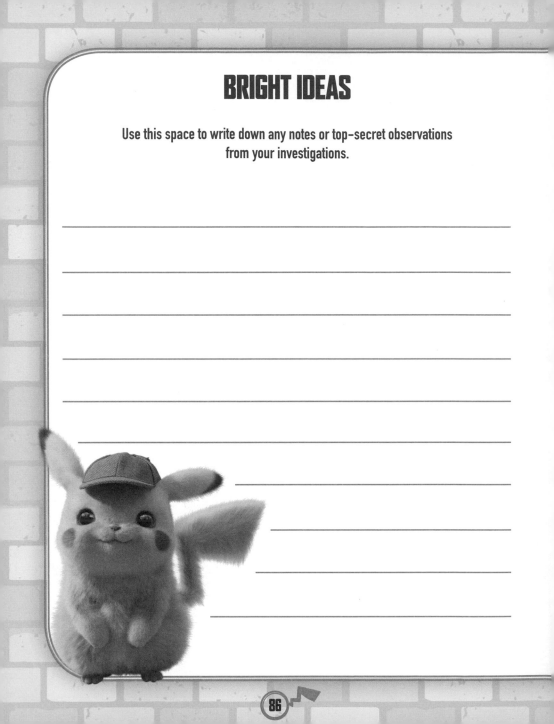

DETECTIVE LICENCE

Now that you have been thoroughly trained, you are ready
to become a detective, just like Detective Pikachu!

Ask an adult to help you
cut out your detective
licence.

RYME CITY

CERTIFICATE OF LICENCE

PRIVATE DETECTIVE

_____

This is to certify that the above-mentioned agent has successfully completed the
detective training programme and is hereby officially licensed with all the rights
and powers thereunto appertaining to law.

SIGNATURE _____